WORLD HERITAGE SITE
Devon and Dorset

FOSSILS & ROCKS
OF THE
JURASSIC COAST

ROBERT WESTWOOD
robert.westwood@virgin.net

NIGEL J. CLARKE PUBLICATIONS

IMPRINT OF

COBBLYME PUBLICATIONS LIMITED

GW00567906

First published in Great Britain in 2003

ISBN 0 907683 84 3

NIGEL J. CLARKE PUBLICATIONS

IMPRINT OF

COBBLYME PUBLICATIONS LIMITED

UNIT 2, RUSSELL HOUSE,
LYM CLOSE, LYME REGIS,
DORSET DT7 3DE

T: 01297 442 513

Printed by Acanthus Press Ltd, Wellington, Somerset.

Geology of the Jurassic Coast

Introduction

For the student of geology there is no better part of the world to study than the British Isles. Now a stable part of the Earth's crust, in the past our islands have witnessed every geological phenomenon. Huge volcanoes have poured forth their fiery concoctions, vast deltas and deserts have held sway and towering mountains have risen from the sediments of deep sea troughs.

To the geologist, tracing these events is a challenging detective story. Although much knowledge can be gained by sophisticated scientific techniques, there is still nothing more useful to the geologist than a good exposure of rock. The coastline of East Devon and Dorset provides a wonderful opportunity for the geologist to unravel events in a crucial era of geological history. It is a colourful and exciting history, and fully justifies the awarding of a "World Heritage Site" status.

This guide seeks to give a brief outline of this remarkable history and to explain some of the geology in simple, everyday terms. It details what can be seen at the major locations and discusses how features of the present landscape have arisen.

The Jurassic Coast is a stunningly beautiful area, and it is my belief that a little understanding of how it was formed is within everybody's reach and can only enhance that beauty.

Pictured above – cliffs at Burton Bradstock looking westwards towards West Bay.

Some simple geology

Geology is a relatively modern science. It seems strange that the great thinkers of the Renaissance did not see the remains of sea creatures in rocks well above sea level and come to the conclusions we now readily accept. That view, of course, grossly underestimates the power of the religious beliefs of the time.

Most of the rocks we now see at the top of the Earth's crust are sediments. Some are the remains of riverbeds or desert dunes, but most have been formed from material that collected on the seabed. As the weight of sediment grows, soft sand, mud and clay are gradually turned to solid rock. Animals that live in the sea die, fall to the bottom and their hard parts are sometimes preserved as fossils.

Because the seabed is largely flat, these sediments form flat layers with older layers obviously at the bottom of the sequence. How then do these rocks appear well above sea level? Some have apparently risen thousands of feet; clearly enormous forces have been at work.

The key to understanding this is to realise that the Earth's crust is not static but constantly changing. This should be obvious when we compare the surface of the moon. Craters formed from meteorite impacts millions of years ago remain visible exactly as they were when the meteorites struck. Meteorites struck the Earth too, but the traces have, in almost all cases, been long since erased. We now know that the Earth's crust is constantly moving. Divided up into a number of "plates" and powered by the heat within the Earth, parts of the crust collide, split apart and glide past each other. Continents move, oceans form and are squashed out of existence. All this happens very slowly from a human perspective, but volcanoes and earthquakes bear witness to the huge forces involved.

One of the consequences of this movement is that some parts of the Earth's surface have witnessed many changes. At times they have been under a deep sea, at other times raised above sea level. They have been deltas and deserts, lakes and lagoons. They have been in tropical and arctic climates.

The Earth's atmosphere is another major factor. Once rocks have been raised above sea level they are weathered and eroded by water, wind and ice. Much material is taken back to the sea where it is deposited again and eventually forms part of a new sedimentary rock. A grain of sand we now find lying on a beach may have gone through many such cycles.

The evidence to decipher this history is in the rocks. For example, coral only occurs in shallow tropical seas, so when a geologist finds fossil coral, he or she knows those rocks were deposited in a shallow tropical sea. As I have said, the Jurassic Coast provides a fantastic amount of evidence to help the geologist piece together the events of an important era in the Earth's history, including the intriguing age of the dinosaurs. With a little help, anyone can see and appreciate this evidence for themselves.

The rocks of the Jurassic Coast

The coastline of East Devon and Dorset provides a complete record of sedimentary rocks formed from around 250 million years ago to around 66 million years ago. Geologists divide this time into the Triassic, Jurassic and Cretaceous periods, the Triassic being the oldest and the Cretaceous the youngest. The oldest rocks are to be found in the west with the strata gradually getting younger as we travel eastwards. They are rocks that have formed in a variety of environments and contain much evidence of the range of life at those times. This guide starts with the oldest rocks of the area then selects locations further east to guide the reader through the events of geological history.

Looking westwards towards West Bay from Burton Bradstock. The harder layers in the Bridport Sands can clearly be seen in the cliffs.

The geological history of the Jurassic Coast

The Earth is about 4500 million years old. At around 250 million years old, the oldest rocks we see on the Jurassic Coast are relatively young. Very few really ancient rocks survive, due to the continual recycling of the crust as we discussed before. This helps explain why geological time is divided into eras and periods starting at around 550 million years ago with the Cambrian period, and the preceding time [around 4000 million years] is simply known as the Pre-Cambrian. Another reason is that the Cambrian rocks are the earliest found to contain conspicuous fossils. It is the variety of the fossil record that geologists use to draw the boundary between periods of geological time. It has nothing to do with global events such as mountain building epochs or the separation of continents, although the changes in the flora and fauna often do coincide with such events.

The earliest rocks found on the Jurassic Coast are from the Triassic period. This was a period when much of Britain was

Gad Cliff, Tyneham — looking east from Gad Cliff near Tyneham. The gently dipping Middle Jurassic strata underlying the Portland and Purbeck rocks can be clearly seen. The Purbeck rocks form a hard cap for Gad Cliff, giving it its distinctive and spectacular shape.

land, and mountains lay to the west and north of what is now Devon and Dorset. These mountains had been formed when the two supercontinents of Laurasia and Gondwanaland collided to form Pangaea, resulting in most of the Earth's landmass being concentrated in one huge continent. Devon and Dorset then lay on the boundary between the two earlier supercontinents.

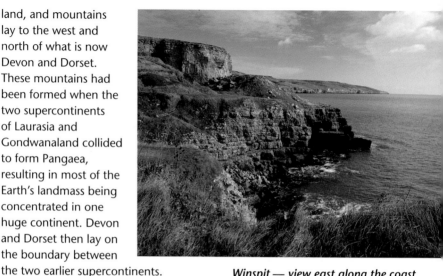

Winspit — view east along the coast showing the horizontal strata of the Portland Stone. These limestones were deposited in shallow, tropical seas.

Following the formation of the mountains there was a long period of desert conditions during which the distinctive Old Red Sandstone of Devon was deposited in the arid plains. In the Triassic period we see sediments from rivers, deltas and shallow salty lakes. Great changes then took place at the beginning of the Jurassic when the sea returned and an era of marine sedimentation began. The level and extent of the sea was controlled by the continuing earth movements, but the sediments and their valuable fossil record continued to collect for many millions of years. Land was never far away, however, and certain times such as the Upper Jurassic and Lower Cretaceous saw shallow lagoon type environments where dinosaurs and other giant reptiles roamed.

By this time the supercontinent of Pangaea had broken up and the south coast of England was once more destined to be on the scene of a continental

collision. The marine sedimentation had taken place in a sea known as the Tethys, which now divided two great continental masses. This continued in the Upper Cretaceous when the chalk was deposited in shallow tropical seas. The end of the Cretaceous saw great changes across the planet. The dinosaurs, along with the ammonites and many other animals, mysteriously died out. The impact of a giant meteorite is now the most favoured explanation for this cataclysm.

The south coast now found itself on the edge of the collision between the Eurasian and African plates. The sediments from this period originated in a variety of environments, alternately marine and non-marine, indicating a sea level that was rising and falling, and serving notice that more intense earth movements were on the way. These culminated in he formation of the Alps where the ediments that had accumulated in the ethys Sea were folded and thrust into a nain of mountains. The effects of these uge earth movements spread far and ride and were responsible for the folds e see now in Stair Hole (Lulworth Cove) nd elsewhere on the Jurassic Coast.

nce these momentous events Dorset has een above sea level and the sediments ave been subject to the forces of erosion. uring the glacial periods the edge of ne ice sheets lay less than a hundred niles to the north, and mighty rivers rould have carried melt-water to the sea during the short summer months. Today the sea continues to wear away at the coast, constantly exposing the remains of creatures dead for millions of years. In places where soft sediments form the cliffs the effects of rain water and waves result in huge landslides.

The juxtaposition of hard and soft sediments has led to some of the unique and beautiful features of the coast such as Lulworth Cove and Worbarrow Bay.

Nature, it seems, has worked over many millennia to form a landscape that delights thousands of visitors each year.

The geological ages of the Jurassic Coast

Mass extinctions — end of the dinosaurs.	65 million years ago	Main outcrops in East Dorset. Chalk and Wealden series of Purbeck.
Great age of dinosaurs — first flowering plants.	**Cretaceous**	
Atlantic Ocean forming, continents broken up. Tropical climates.	144 million years ago	
Many dinosaurs — first birds appear.	**Jurassic**	Much of Dorset coast. Oldest beds in west, Lyme Regis and Charmouth. Youngest in east, Portland and Purbeck series.
Supercontinent of Pangaea begins to break up. Largely tropical conditions.	206 million years ago	
First dinosaurs and mammals.		
Land joined to form supercontinent of Pangaea. Climate hot and dry.	**Triassic**	Rocks of East Devon, Sidmouth, Ladram Bay.
Mass extinctions — 95% of species disappear.	248 million years ago	

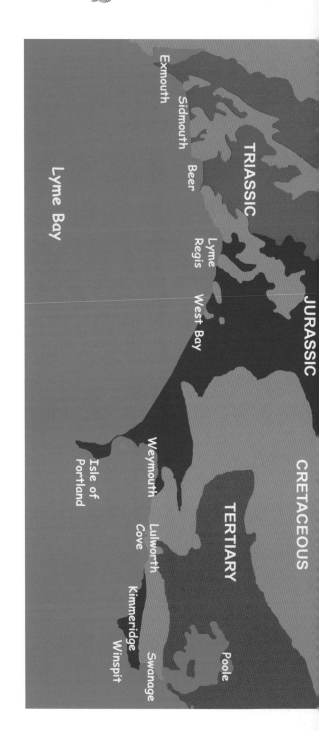

The map above shows the locations of the main sites mentioned in the book, as well as the geological distribution of the landscape. The oldest Triassic rocks are found to the west of the area, with the strata gradually becoming younger as you travel east.

Budleigh Salterton to Sidmouth

Budleigh Salterton, Ladram Bay and Sidmouth

Getting there

Budleigh Salterton is a popular seaside town. There is a large parking area on the eastern side of the town near the river estuary. Ladram Bay is a few miles east of Budleigh Salterton and is accessed by a narrow, winding road. At the end of this is a holiday camp where you can park all day for a very reasonable rate. The coastal footpath towards Budleigh Salterton rewards the walker with some wonderful views over the bay. Sidmouth is another busy holiday resort with a number of car parks giving easy access to the beach.

What to see

* At the bottom of the cliffs on the western edge of the beach at Budleigh Salterton you should be able to find the Budleigh Salterton Pebble Beds. The name is enough to distinguish this formation as it consists of many rounded pebbles held loosely together by a sandstone cement. This marks the beginning of the Triassic period about 250 million years ago, a truly momentous time in the Earth's history. Most land was embraced by the supercontinent of Pangaea and vast tracts were hot, barren deserts. At the end of the preceding period, the Permian, 99% of all life on the planet had died out. We are still not sure why. Mighty mountains had been thrust up as plates collided to form Pangaea, and these now began to be eroded. In this part of Devon rivers were bringing the eroded material onto arid plains.

* The Budleigh Salterton Pebble Beds were deposited by fairly fast flowing rivers. We can tell this from the size of the pebbles; the faster the river, the bigger the pebbles it can carry along. The fact that the pebbles are well rounded suggests that they have been subject to a number of cycles of erosion and transportation.

* Above the Pebble Beds we find a thick sequence of sandstones deposited in continental conditions. By this we mean that they were laid down in river channels, on flood

The Budleigh Salterton Pebble Beds deposited by fast flowing rivers at the start of the Triassic period.

plains, in shallow lakes, or by the action of wind. Look carefully at the cliffs and you will see examples of what is known as cross-bedding. This is where thin bedding planes seem to cut across one another, and is the result of sands being deposited in a river channel which shifts its position over time. Sometimes, slightly harder layers in the rocks pick this out even more clearly.

＊ At Ladram Bay the Triassic sands have been eroded to form a beautiful bay with stacks marking the former line of the coast. Cross-bedding can clearly be seen in the cliffs here, and harder layers containing more calcium carbonate help distinguish the almost horizontal bedding plains.

*adram Bay — cross-bedding is clearly
vident in the sandstone cliffs*

adram Bay — Triassic sandstone cliffs and stacks at Ladram Bay

* Sidmouth is a town with considerable old-world charm and a traditional seaside atmosphere. It too provides impressive sandstone cliffs, although they are currently very unstable and are best viewed from a distance.

* There are other places of geological interest on this part of the Devon coast. A few miles east of Sidmouth lies the picturesque village of Branscombe. A tiny, winding road leads to a rambling settlement that oozes charm. The road finishes at a grassy car park behind the beach, where it is possible to appreciate one of the key geological features of the Jurassic Coast. To the west of the mouth of the tiny river the red cliffs of the Triassic sandstones are again visible. Look east from here, however, and you will see something entirely different. In the distance is the unmistakable sight of the chalk at its most westerly outcrop, near the small fishing village of Beer. In between, and geologically speaking, underneath the chalk, are more Cretaceous sands, silts and limestones. If you have remembered the geological timescale correctly, you might wonder where the Jurassic rocks have disappeared. The fact is they were completely eroded in this part of the world before the Cretaceous rocks were laid down.

It is tempting to think of rock formations as following on from one another seamlessly simply because they lie next to each other. In fact, millions of years of erosion followed the last Jurassic rocks before those of the Cretaceous began to be deposited. This is seen particularly well in the west of the Jurassic Coast where all the rocks which give the region its name have been worn away! This is known as the Cretaceous overstep, and we meet it again in Lyme Bay.

The chalk cliffs of Beer Head

Lyme Bay to Charmouth

Lyme Bay to Charmouth

The Cobb — looking towards Charmouth

Getting there

To access the cliffs west of the harbour at Lyme Regis follow the signs to the Cobb and the car park at Monmouth Beach. For the cliffs east of the harbour you can either walk along the front from Monmouth Beach [about 10-15 minutes] or park in the large car park on the road out of Lyme Regis on the east side.

What to see

❋ Famous throughout the world as a fossil collecting paradise, the geology of Lyme Bay has plenty of other fascinating information for those interested in the Earth's history. The gently dipping strata, deposited in shallow seas, tell us much about conditions at the time, while the wealth of fossil remains give a very detailed picture of life in those ancient oceans.

❋ At Monmouth Beach, so-called because it was the landing site of the ill-fated rebellion led by the Duke of Monmouth, the cliffs are largely composed of rocks known as the Blue Lias. These are rocks from early on in the Jurassic when Dorset was just north of the tropics and the Atlantic Ocean was beginning to open up.

Notice how the layers of rock slope gently to the east, again evidence of earth movements at a later stage.

* Notice also how there are harder beds of a clayey limestone at frequent intervals, with softer clay and silt in between. We see this at other places on the coast and it is evidence of an environment changing in a rhythmical way. Possibly the sea level changed or the climate. The rocks here are dark grey in colour and are the source rocks in which oil deposits formed indicating a sea floor poor in oxygen.

Monmouth Beach, Lyme Regis — the gently dipping strata of the Lower Lias rocks can clearly be seen. Note the ammonite in the boulder.

* Much of the material for these sediments probably came from the mountains of Devon and Cornwall. Land cannot have been far away, as the well known finds of land-living dinosaurs testify. What is certain is that these seas teemed with life. Walk along the beach at low tide and look for the remains of large ammonites in boulders; imagine them swimming around with their smaller cousins, together with fish and marine reptiles like the famous ichthyosaur. What we do not see so much evidence for, of course, are the smaller and soft bodied organisms that must have provided the vast amount of material for the lower part of the food chain.

* On a clear day the cliffs stretching eastwards from Lyme Regis present a magnificent sight. Golden Cap, the highest cliff in the south of England, stands out and illustrates an important geological feature. Its name comes from its cap of golden sandstone, formed in the much more recent Cretaceous period. The cliffs between Lyme Regis and Charmouth have a similar cap. It may be difficult to see because of the vegetation and crumbling of the cliffs, but the near horizontal Cretaceous rocks lie on top of the sloping Jurassic rocks. This is the "unconformity" that we met at Branscombe, where the Jurassic rocks have been uplifted and eroded before the sea invaded again and more sediment was deposited. Millions of years elapsed between the deposition of these rocks which now lie one on top of the other.

✳ It is still possible to collect good fossils from the beaches around Lyme Regis and there are several excellent guides to help you do this. Ammonites, of course, are common, as are belemnites. The bones of reptiles can also be found, but extensive remains are rare. There is no need to dig in the cliffs as the constant erosion provides a continual supply of new material. On a recent visit to Monmouth Beach it was noticeable how many limestone pebbles near the cliffs had been split by fossil hunters.

Charmouth — the beach at Charmouth showing a harder, limestone layer sticking out of the largely clay cliffs.

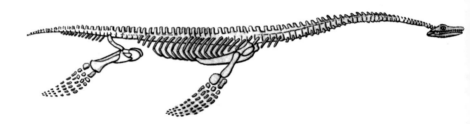

Bridport and West Bay

Bridport and West Bay

Getting there

West Bay is a short distance south of Bridport. Follow the signs from the ring road south of the town and park in the large car park on the left just before the harbour. Walk around the harbour and down to the beach. Eype can be reached by car from the Bridport to Charmouth road. There is a small car park near the beach.

What to see

✳ West Bay is a small, attractive village and holiday resort built around a busy harbour. The harbour was built in 1722. There is an interesting museum by the harbour side.

✳ The towering sandstone cliffs have been much photographed, particularly in the winter months when early and late sun produces a wonderful golden glow. The rocks here are known as the Bridport Sands and are part of the Upper Lias division of the Jurassic. The horizontal layers can clearly be seen in the cliffs and were formed on the bottom of a shallow tropical sea. Some of the layers are harder than others and these clearly stand out. They represent different conditions, with the harder layers possibly indicating

West Bay, Bridport — the busy working harbour

West Bay, Bridport — the stunning, vertical cliffs at West Bay are formed from the Bridport Sands. The horizontal layers are clearly visible thanks to the presence of harder, more cemented sandstones

a stormier environment when more organic material was collected on the seabed and there was less chance for fine clay to settle. The fact that these layers repeat up the cliff suggests the conditions varied in a rhythmical way.

❋ The golden cliffs are capped by a thin layer of limestone known as the Inferior Oolite. This is an interesting rock formed from tiny ooliths, spherical grains of calcium carbonate that grew around a grain of sand or shell fragment. The rolling action of waves on ancient sandbanks has produced limestone that appears to consist of millions of tiny ball bearings.

The Middle Lias sands at Eype's Mouth glow in the late evening sun

❋ Eype is a tiny village just east of West Bay. At Eype's Mouth we see good sections through the silts and sands of the Middle Lias. Remember at Lyme we saw largely silts and clays from the Lower Lias, indicative of relatively quiet marine environments. Now it seems things were not so quiet; the sea may have been shallower and subject periodically to storms. At the top of the silts and sands is the Eype Clay, probably deposited in quieter conditions. This finishes with the famous Starfish Bed, which contains many broken specimens of brittle-stars. This is thought to have been caused by storm conditions which resulted in vast amounts of sediment being brought to the sea, overwhelming the aptly named starfish. You may find broken bits of these creatures, but complete specimens are very rare.

Portland and Chesil Beach

Portland and Chesil Beach

Getting there

From Weymouth follow the signs to Portland. Once you are on the "island" follow the signs to the castle. As you reach the Portland Heights Hotel at the top of the hill there are free car parks from where there are wonderful views across Chesil Beach. You can also set off southwards on the coast footpath and quickly come to vast, old quarry workings that you can explore. From the hotel follow the road to Portland Bill where there is a large car park.

What to see

※ The first thing most people view when visiting Portland is the impressive eighteen mile sweep of Chesil Beach, famous to geography students everywhere as a classic example of a tombolo, a sand or shingle bar connecting two areas of land. It has been formed as storm waves sweep pebbles from west to east.

※ The west cliffs [follow the coast path from the Portland Heights Hotel] show the landslipped Portland Sand capped by the harder Portland Stone. This sequence represents a shallowing of a muddy sea to clear, warm tropical seas with clean, white limesand on the bottom. The quarries at the top of the west cliffs extracted the Portland Stone that formed under these idyllic conditions. The gentle, rolling action of the waves on these ancient sandbanks led to the formation of a very distinctive limestone known as oolite, consisting of tiny spherical ooliths. The effect is of a rock made of minute ball bearings cemented together; the word oolite is derived from the Greek word for fish roe. Examine a broken bit carefully and you should be able to see these ooliths.

※ Portland Bill is perhaps the best place to see the Portland Stone. Here were the quarries from which the superb building stone was shipped to such projects as St. Paul's Cathedral. The stone dips gently down into the sea and was quarried directly from the shoreline. Walk across the top of the layers in the limestone and you are walking on the bed of an ancient, tropical sea. On some layers you can see the remains of hundreds of fossilised oysters. Also at Portland Bill is a fine example of a raised beach. The ledge of limestone above the present sea level shows where the level was during the Pleistocene period a few million years ago.

※ To finish your visit here, stand on the cliffs at Portland Bill looking northeastwards towards the Dorset coast. Imagine the Portland strata rising gently to the north across the sea and then plunging steeply down on the distant coastline. This was the structure produced by the Alpine earth movements before the forces of erosion did their work.

Portland Bill — waves batter Pulpit Rock on the edge of the old quarry workings

Looking westwards from Portland over Chesil Beach

Portland Bill lighthouse seen from the old quarry workings on the cliffs.

Lulworth Cove

Lulworth Cove

Getting there

Known to every student of geology and geography, Lulworth Cove is one of the most visited field trip locations in the country. Follow the signs to Lulworth Cove and park in the large [and expensive] car park at the entrance to the village. From here footpaths lead westwards over the cliff to Durdle Door, eastwards to the bay and just south of the car park to Stair Hole. Follow the path around the bay and up the cliff and you will shortly find signs to the famous "fossil forest".

Looking east from Durdle Door — a view along the coast east of Durdle Door showing the impressive Chalk cliffs

What to see

❋ The first thing to do is visit the information centre by the car park, which has an excellent display explaining local geology. The rocks at Lulworth range from those at the top of the Jurassic period [Portland and Purbeck beds] to the chalk of the Cretaceous period. An explanation of the conditions in which these rocks were formed is given elsewhere; at Lulworth it is the structures that are so fascinating.

❋ The first thing to notice at Lulworth is that the layers of rock [strata] lie vertically or near vertically, rather than horizontally. Remember, these are again mostly sediments deposited on a flat sea floor; tremendous earth movements have been involved in contorting them to a near vertical position. The rocks at Lulworth form part of a gigantic step fold, the top of which has been eroded away. This probably happened as a result of pressure from the south as Africa continued to collide with Europe.

❋ The older Portland and Purbeck rocks underneath the Chalk appear at the south of the cove. The rocks between these and the Chalk are much softer, so once the sea broke through the harder rocks, it quickly scoured away the bay within the softer rocks. The stream flowing through the village was once a much larger watercourse and this must have broken through the Portland and Purbeck rocks where the mouth of the bay now is.

❋ Further evidence of huge earth movements can be seen at Stair

Lulworth Cove — a picturesque bay cut out of the soft sands and clays of the Cretaceous Wealden Beds; the resistant chalk forms the back of the bay. In the foreground are the steeply dipping Purbeck rocks.

Hole. Here Purbeck strata have been compressed into crumple folds which can be seen clearly in the cliff face. Formed at the same time as the bigger step fold, they represent small crumples within the overall larger structure. It is difficult to imagine how solid rocks can deform in this manner. Common sense seems to tell us that hard, brittle rock would simply shatter under intense pressure, not flow into graceful folds as if it were plasticene. However we should not forget that these rocks were deep underground when they were deformed. A lot of heat would be generated too, and under these conditions the rocks behave in a much more fluid manner.

Stair Hole, Lulworth Cove — the famous crumple fold in the thinly bedded Purbeck rocks, caused by earth movements at the time of the Alpine mountain building episode.

✳ To the east of Lulworth
Cove can be seen the
Fossil Forest. Here, visible
in the Purbeck rocks, are
the fossilised remains
of tree stumps [largely
empty moulds] and
round formations known
as stromatolites. These are the
fossilised remains of algal growth
around fallen trees and stumps. It
is fascinating to think as you look at
these features that you are standing
in what was once a salty, shallow
lagoon where dinosaurs waded
through watery forests.

Fossil Forest, Lulworth — this stromatolite is the result of algal growth around the base of a rotting tree in the swamps of the Purbeck period.

Worbarrow Bay

Worbarrow Bay

Getting there

Worbarrow Bay is best accessed from the ruined village of Tyneham, reached from a minor road east of the B3070 at East Lulworth. The village was requisitioned by the army in the build-up to D-Day, and stands as a museum to life in an early twentieth century village. It is an atmospheric place, and speaks volumes for the fortitude of people who made a meagre living off the land, sea and estates of the wealthy. The area is still part of an army firing range and is not always open, although it usually is at weekends and holidays. It is best to check beforehand on 01929 552740. There is a large free car park from which it is a short walk down to the coast at Worbarrow.

sweep of the beach. You are standing on the relatively hard Purbeck rocks at the very top of the Jurassic period. These, as described elsewhere, are largely limestones formed in freshwater lagoons on the edge of land. Sometimes very shallow, they represent the archetypal marshland where giant dinosaurs once tramped.

The broad sweep of Worbarrow Bay, formed from the relatively soft Cretaceous rocks deposited in river deltas and shallow seas. These lie in between the much harder Purbeck limestones to the south and the pure limestone of the chalk to the north.

What to see

* Worbarrow is an excellent place to study and appreciate the geology of the Purbecks. Here the whole sequence of rocks, which in the area around Swanage stretches over several miles, is condensed into a much shorter cross-section.

* To best understand, place yourself at Worbarrow Tout at the southern end of the bay and look across the broad

* The Purbeck rocks lie almost vertical, thrown up and contorted by giant earth movements associated with the movements of the vast "plates" of the Earth's crust. Consequently, as we look northwards, we see the rocks deposited above them. These are much softer sands and clays, initially laid down in a huge delta. These are followed by marine sandstones, and eventually by the Chalk, a rock

Worbarrow Bay

composed almost entirely of the calcareous remains of tiny organisms that lived in a clear, shallow sea. The Chalk is much harder, and accounts for the shape of the bay where the softer rocks have been eroded more quickly. This general structure can be appreciated from almost anywhere in the Purbecks. Follow the coast road and you will be on top of the ridge formed by the hard Purbeck and Portland limestones; to the north you can see the valley formed from the softer clays and sands, while beyond lies the Chalk ridge.

✳ It is worth a close look around the Purbeck rocks at Worbarrow Tout. Examine the top of the exposed layers and you may be lucky enough to spot the traces of dinosaur footprints, typically from the three-pronged feet of the iguanodon. They are not easy to find on surfaces which are naturally uneven, but if you find something which may be interesting, let your imagination do the rest!

Worbarrow Tout — steeply dipping Purbeck strata

Kimmeridge Bay

Kimmeridge Bay

Clavell Tower, Kimmeridge Bay — a well-known folly on the eastern end of the bay

Getting there
Follow the signs to Kimmeridge and park in the large car park at the top of the cliffs. A small gully leads down to the beach.

What to see

❋ Kimmeridge Bay is another classic location for geologists, and gives its name to a sequence of clays near the top of the Jurassic period. At this time much of Britain was covered by an extensive sea, where sediments accumulated undisturbed for millions of years. The cliffs here show gently dipping strata of marine origin containing many fossils. These fossils have often been flattened by the weight of sediment as it continued to collect on the sea bed, and it has been estimated that the thickness of the sediment has been reduced by a factor of about eight as it has been compacted into rock. Looking at the cliffs now it is staggering to think how much sediment collected in this ancient sea!

❋ The cliffs at Kimmeridge show alternating bands of harder and

Kimmeridge Bay — harder ledges in the Kimmeridge beds resist erosion and stretch out to sea. They represent ancient sea floors and show the marks of scouring by currents. Walk on here and you are walking along the bottom of a Jurassic ocean.

softer rocks. We have seen before how this indicates an environment changing in a rhythmical or cyclical way. There has been much discussion about the cause of these cycles, and the extensive exposure of strata at Kimmeridge means this is an almost unique location to study this phenomenon.

❋ The rate at which sediment accumulated is, of course, a major factor, since once this has been established the variation in the strata can be correlated with other events. It has been estimated that the rocks at Kimmeridge collected at the rate of about 3 cm every thousand years; an amazing thought when

you stand at the bottom of the cliffs! It is clear that whatever caused the cycles in the rocks operated within

The sweep of Kimmeridge Bay showing the gently dipping Kimmeridge Clays

a time scale of many thousands of years, perhaps something like 30 – 40 thousand years. One suggestion is that this is related to the change in the angle of tilt of the Earth's axis which occurs within a similar time scale. This results in the climate belts of the Earth moving and would thus have had an effect on the rate of sedimentation.

Many fossils can be found in the Kimmeridge Clay, including ammonites, belemnites and lamellibranchs. The bones of giant marine and flying reptiles have also been found.

At the end of the Kimmeridge Clay the sea retreated and apart from southern England much of Britain was land. In the shallow seas to the south of the new landmass, the Portland Beds began to form.

Looking towards Kimmeridge from Gad Cliff — note the dipping Jurassic strata

Winspit and Durlston Bay

Winspit and Durlston Bay

Winspit - view east along the coast over the ledges cut by the quarrying of Portland Stone. Note the thick, horizontally bedded Portland beds.

Getting there

Winspit is accessed from the small village of Worth Matravers, a few miles west of Swanage. There is a small car park at the entrance to the village from where you can follow one of the footpaths through the village down to Winspit. Durlston Bay is a short walk from the main car park at the southern end of Swanage. Follow the signs to Peveril Point.

What to see

* Winspit is a spectacular place to visit. Cut into the Portland Stone are giant caves from where the valuable building stone was once quarried and loaded onto barges before being transferred to larger ships. It is easy to imagine what a hazardous occupation this was. Here the rocks clearly lie in horizontal beds, in stark contrast to nearby Worbarrow and Lulworth where they are nearly vertical. Remember that this part of the coast lies further south and you might realise that we are seeing the horizontal part of the step fold we mentioned earlier. Further north the Portland and Purbeck beds dip steeply downwards [the vertical part of the step].

Caves at Winspit

❋ At the end of the Kimmeridge stage of the Jurassic, the sea retreated and in this part of Britain the relatively

Winspit — the large fossil ammonite in the foreground is an example known as Titanites, and is the zone fossil for the Portland strata.

deep sea of the Kimmeridge Clay gave way to a much more shallow sea. Here, in the warm waters, a solid limestone was deposited, the calcium carbonate coming from the remains of organisms that lived there Uniquely in the Portland rocks we find the giant ammonite that appears in the walls of public buildings and some houses of the area, the aptly named Titanites.

❋ At Durlston we find the classic exposure of the Purbeck rocks. The junction between the Jurassic and the Cretaceous periods lies somewhere in these strata. At the end of the Portland the sea retreated again and in Dorset a giant lagoon was separated from the sea and became freshwater. We know this from the type of fossils which are found there. It has been estimated that the lagoon was typically about a metre deep, and often dried out completely. In these conditions thin beds of limestone were formed with the shells of many molluscs obvious in some layers.

❋ Trees grew in this lagoon as we saw at the fossil forest near Lulworth, and dinosaurs once roamed here. It is still possible to find the imprints of their giant feet, particularly the three-pronged foot of the iguanodon Have a look first in the museum near the old quay in Swanage and you will know what to look for. Remember, when you look at the top of one of the layers, you are looking at the bottom of the lagoon at a particular time; this is where to look for footprints.

Durlston Bay — view of cliffs showing thinly bedded Purbeck strata, gently dipping into the cliff. These are rocks deposited in shallow, freshwater lagoons, occasionally showing the outlines of dinosaur footprints.

Peveril Point — these dipping Purbeck strata provide a wonderful example of a geological feature known as a plunging syncline.

Finish your visit here on the beach under the coastguard station at Peveril Point. Here thin ledges of limestone stretch out to sea dipping in towards each other. These strata are part of a syncline, a u-shaped fold formed during the earth movements that have caused other contortions in the rocks of the Dorset coast. This one is also tilted so that the strata appear to curve around and meet up a little way off shore. You can visualise this if you take a piece of paper, fold it gently along its length and then tilt it. Now try drawing a horizontal line on the paper and see what shape it makes. This is the shape you see in the strata at Peveril Point.

A brief guide to fossils

Fossils are the remains of living things preserved in rocks. They can take many forms but it is almost always the hard parts of animals and plants that are preserved. Actual shell or bone may survive or simply the casts and moulds produced by these hard parts. They might be transformed into some other substance by the process of chemical replacement. This is how we get beautiful ammonites made out of fool's gold [iron pyrites]. It might seem a somewhat miraculous process but is simply the result of the original shell being dissolved away and then another chemical crystallising out in the mould that is left.

We also regard the marks and tracks left by animals as fossils. Along the Jurassic Coast we see burrows and trails left by crustaceans and, more excitingly, dinosaur footprints in the lagoonal deposits of the Purbeck.

Our journey along the Jurassic Coast starts at a crucial time in the history of life on Earth. A mass extinction at the end of the Permian period had wiped out 99% of species. No wonder then that the wonderful exposures of rocks from subsequent ages has helped us document and understand the evolution and diversification of life from that pivotal moment.

In the Triassic period we see the first true ammonites and the bullet shaped belemnites; these being two examples of the still successful molluscs. Vertebrates evolved into many different species. There were fish, amphibians, reptiles and early mammals. The world's land was still joined in the supercontinent of Pangaea. The climate was generally warm throughout the huge land mass and there were few barriers to the migration of animals. This helps explain why animals and plants were largely the same all over the world. The most common plants were tall conifer trees; these evolved many new forms by the end of the period. It is, of course, in the Triassic that we see the first dinosaurs [terrible reptiles]. The first of these animals that have aroused such curiosity and interest were small meat eaters that ran about on their hind legs. Towards the end of the Triassic we see the first mammals, and coincidentally, the first crocodiles; a group today that perhaps still deserves the title "terrible reptile"!

Also in the Triassic there appeared a marine reptile that was to abound in the Jurassic seas, the Ichthyosaur. These "fish reptiles" evolved from continental reptiles and became efficient, streamlined hunters. First discovered by the legendary fossil collector Mary Anning of Lyme Regis, examples can be seen today in the fossil shops of the town.

In the Jurassic period the great continent

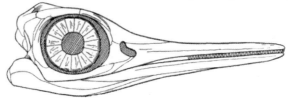

f Pangaea began to break up. The climate was still generally warm and conifers and primitive plants covered the land. This was the age when the dinosaurs evolved into many different forms and dominated life on land. Towards the end of the period the first birds appeared.

Due to the break-up of Pangaea there were more shallow marine environments for living things to colonise. Many new species of shellfish evolved. Ammonites and belemnites were common, and there were many marine reptiles. There were many animals, too, that made a living in the mud of the sea floor. Some bivalves burrowed into the sea floor and we sometimes see these burrows preserved today as trace fossils.

Extensive seas covered much of Europe in the Jurassic, but towards the end of the period things began to change again. In the area that is now the south coast of England a shallow fresh water lagoon environment formed, followed later in the Cretaceous period by huge deltas. It is in these environments, on or close to land, that we find the remains of the remarkable reptiles that once roamed the swamps and forests of the Cretaceous landscape.

As Pangaea continued to split up during the Cretaceous there were more marine environments for life to exploit. Ammonites continued to evolve and other groups of shellfish such as gastropods diversified. Many creatures now inhabited the seabed, and carnivores like crabs and lobsters hunted the shellfish.

On land the Cretaceous saw the evolution of the flowering plants, which have continued to dominate the plant kingdom ever since. Dinosaurs continued to dominate but new groups of mammals evolved and became more and more successful.

Later on in the Cretaceous period, marine conditions returned again to southern Britain and the extensive chalk seas teemed with a variety of reptiles, fish, crustaceans and shellfish. Things were to change dramatically at the end of the period as another great mass extinction wiped out around fifty per cent of the world's species, including all the dinosaurs and ammonites. There have been many theories to explain this momentous event, interest sparked, of course, by the sudden disappearance of the dinosaurs. Any theory must also explain many other extinctions; the most favoured one currently being the collision of the Earth with a large asteroid. A major factor in this theory is that it explains the concentration of the rare element iridium in sediments formed at the end of the Cretaceous. Iridium is extremely rare on Earth, but is relatively much more common in meteorites. If our planet had been struck by a giant meteorite or asteroid it would account for this "iridium layer".

It is strange that our journey through geological history along the Jurassic Coast should end as it began, with a mass extinction of many of the Earth's species. In between, many groups of wonderful creatures evolved and died out. Thanks to the wonderful fossil record of the Devon and Dorset coast we now know a great deal about this "lost world".

The Ammonites

Of all the fossils associated with the Jurassic Coast, the ammonite is perhaps the most well known. Local fossil shops sell them in their hundreds, some beautifully replaced by iron pyrites, giving the impression of a creature turned to

Dorset Ammonites

gold. To the geologist they are, indeed, often worth their weight in gold.

Ammonites appear at the beginning of the Jurassic period around 200 million years ago. They are cephalopod molluscs related to the octopus and squid, although their closest living relative is the nautilus. They were free-swimming creatures, using the chambers in their shells as ballast tanks to control buoyancy. The soft parts of the animal itself were located in the end chamber. Judging by the number of fossils we now find, they must have

been a common sight floating about the Jurassic and Cretaceous seas in various shapes and sizes.

Despite being common, ammonites are very special fossils, of enormous use to the geologists trying to work out the history of these ancient times. The reason for this is that ammonites evolved very quickly and so are important in helping to identify rocks as being from a particular age.

To understand why this is so important it must be remembered that the type of rock that forms depends on its geographical location. Different sediments are now forming in the English Channel and North Sea. In millions of years' time, after these sediments have compacted to form rocks, they may look totally different. It may be that the skeletal remains of cod, plaice, herring and so on will confirm that they originated at around the same time. However, if these fish all survive unchanged for millions of years, it may not help the future geologist at all!

This is why ammonites are so valuable. Individual species did not last long before they evolved into different species. When we find them in two different rocks therefore, they tell us that those rocks are of the same age. For example, the giant ammonite Titanites, seen in many garden walls in the Isle of Purbeck, lived at the time when the Portland rocks were being deposited. Find an example of Titanites in a rock and you know how old that rock is. Thus

...nmonites are an important example of ...hat are known as zone fossils.

...hat makes ammonites even more ...scinating to the amateur geologist ...that the evolutionary trends are ...latively easy to pick out. It seems that ...s ammonites evolved they developed ...ore and more ornamentation on ...ie outside of their shells, so generally ...beaking, the ones with smooth shells ...e earlier than those with spikes and ...iobbly bits on. Another trend involved ...ie walls that separated the chambers ...i the ammonite shell. These gradually ...ecame more and more elaborate, and if ...bu are lucky enough to find an example, ...rm beautifully intricate patterns on the ...utside where the shell has worn away.

At the end of the Cretaceous [around 60 million years ago] the ammonites, like the dinosaurs, mysteriously disappear. By that time they had seemingly gone into evolutionary reverse, with some forms beginning to uncoil, eventually resulting in forms that were almost straight.

The Jurassic seas, where much of Dorset originated, must once have swarmed with these beautiful creatures with their elaborate ornamentation and possibly vibrant colours. They proliferated in rich, tropical seas, and due to their free-swimming lifestyle have left their imprint in a variety of rocks. Today their beauty is still apparent as they provide us with the rare thrill of discovery on Dorset's beaches.

The Dinosaurs

About 225 million years ago the first dinosaur appeared in the forests of what is now South America. It was a small two-legged animal about the size of a chicken. It was quick and agile on its two strong legs, and probably a very effective hunter. Within about 30 million years, its dinosaur relatives had become the dominant creatures on the planet; they were to reign for about 165 million years.

There is often confusion about what a dinosaur actually is. Most people know that it is a reptile, but many also erroneously assume that the term applies to all giant reptiles. In fact dinosaurs came in all shapes and sizes; but certainly some of the larger ones were the biggest, fastest and most ferocious animals that have ever walked the Earth. The main distinguishing feature of a dinosaur is that it is a reptile that developed an upright gait. This gave it an immediate advantage over other reptiles with their awkward sideways gait.

At the beginning of the Triassic period there was a mass extinction of many species. These events have happened a number of times during geological history and have continued to puzzle geologists. Certainly much competition to the emerging dinosaurs was removed by this global catastrophe. The dinosaurs diversified rapidly during the Triassic, and with little competition, got bigger and bigger. Other reptiles also evolved, some taking to the air.

During the Jurassic dinosaurs diversified and became truly dominant. Huge plant-eating varieties evolved along with ferocious predators. Other forms of life also flourished, and in the sea, other reptiles grew to immense size. The shallow, tropical seas in which Dorset's rocks were deposited must have been home to a fantastic array of life.

The Cretaceous period saw dinosaurs continue to dominate. Some of the most well known dinosaurs like Tyrannosaurus lived in this period and the shallow lagoons where the Purbeck rocks were

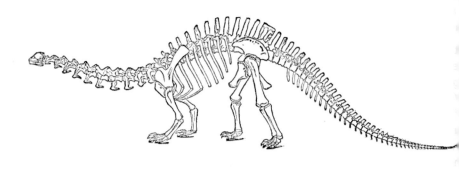

Skeleton of a Brontosaurus

rmed have helped preserve their bones
r us to study. At Durlston Bay and
Vorbarrow Bay it is possible to see the
otprints of these massive creatures.
he most likely example you will find is

Iguanodon bernissartensis
This dinosaur once lived on the Isle of
Purbeck, where its footprints are found in
the stone quarries.

e three-pronged footprint of
e Iguanodon, a plant eater that
as up to 10 metres long and 5
etres high.

the end of the Cretaceous
eriod [about 65 million years
jo] the dinosaurs died out.
hether or not it was the impact
a huge meteorite as has been
ggested is still open to debate.
he evidence is strong, but it
ould be remembered, as we
ave said before, that mass extinctions
ave taken place at other times.

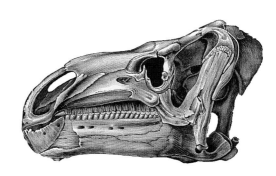

Skull and mandible of
Iguanodon bernissartensis

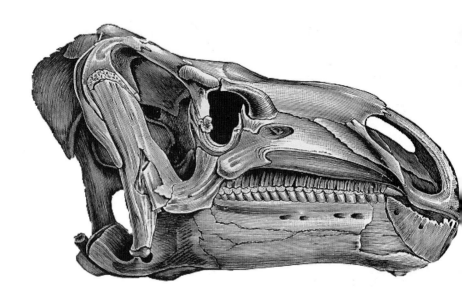